OUR FAMILY

A Personal Record

THIS IS A CARLTON BOOK

Text and design copyright © 1997 Carlton Books Limited

This edition published by Carlton Books Limited 1997
20 St Anne's Court, Wardour Street, London W1V 3AW

A CIP catalogue for this book is available from the British Library

ISBN 1 85868 321 1

Project Editor: Sarah Larter
Art Editor: Zoë Maggs
Designer: Kaye Lyall
Picture research: Rachel Leach
Production: Alexia Rencricca

Printed in Italy

OUR FAMILY
A Personal Record

Karen and Martin Fido

SEVENOAKS

For our dearest cousin,
Margaret Townsend Warren

Contents

Introduction

Starting to trace your family history

Do you live where your grandparents lived? Probably not. Most of us have had to "get on our bikes" and look for work. But your grandparents probably lived pretty close to where their grandparents came from.

Are you a true-born English man or woman? A pure Celt from Scotland or Wales or Ireland? Are you sure? Is your Englishness Ancient woad-painted British? Or Yugoslavian via some settling Roman legionary? Or Anglo-Saxon or Jutish Germanic, or Norman or Huguenot French, or Dutch with the Orangeman or Spanish or Italian from a variety of ways into the country? You're pretty certain to be a mix of several of these.

Did you know that although the Celts shared a language and culture but were not an ethnic group at all, so you may be a Viking Scotsman or a Romano-British descended Welshwoman?

Or are you one of the more recent immigrant additions to our rich mix of national identities? Perhaps a Jewish Briton whose ancestors fled the Russian pogroms, or Bismarck or Hitler? A West Indian whose family arrival in United Kingdom can be timed precisely to the docking of the British Government sponsored immigrant ship *Empire Windrush*? An Asian expelled from East Africa, or perhaps a refugee from the anticipated Communist reorganization of Hong Kong?

There is a curiosity inherent in all of us that makes us ask, "Where did I spring from and what makes me what I am today?"

The heredity *versus* environment argument may continue unabated, but scientists still discover ways in which we are products of our heredity. Studies of twins separated at birth prove beyond doubt that inherited genes play a huge role in determining our natures. In the case of the Argyll family, characteristic handwriting has passed down from one generation to another. Those who were adopted at birth search with great dedication for their biological families, deeming this essential for true self-knowledge.

But the best reason for tracing your family tree is that genealogy is fun. Imagine you have just bought an antique desk. How much more you will cherish it if you know who owned it and when and where! Just think of learning that a great piece of literature was written by a famous author seated at your very own desk!

Sometimes surprising physical artefacts are retained over decades, giving a strange sense of continuity. The brass and mahogany medicine chest of a Cornish doctor in the Crimean War passed to his unmarried granddaughter, who in turn gave it, old dried-up drugs and all, to another Cornish doctor's unmarried doctor daughter. That Victorian object links the Crimean War with the generation surviving the First World War. It shows lasting family friendships among brother-professionals in remote places. It leaps from Victorian patriarchy to the modern professional woman.

Of course an ancestor need not have been a doctor or a soldier. You may be more aware of the great-grandfather who wasted the family fortune on riotous living; the great-great-uncle who did a little embezzling and went to prison or was transported to a far-away colony…

But snobbery has no place in genealogy, for almost everyone also has royal blood. The difficulty lies in tracing it! All genealogists know that if we could follow our ancestry back to Genesis we would find we are all one family – the family of mankind. Some lines of descent can be traced back further than others since, for various reasons, people adopted surnames at different times in history. But we must understand that no one family is really older than any other. This was a point well made when the former Prime Minister Sir Alec Douglas-Home, weary of being taunted as "the Fourteenth Earl" observed that, looked at in that way, Harold Wilson was "the fourteenth Mr Wilson"!

The earliest genealogies are those of royal and sacred families. In Japan, royal and noble lineage has been recorded through the male line since the beginning of written records – a very long time indeed. There are Chinese people alive who can trace their descent through seventy-six generations to the great sage Confucius himself; and he was born in 51 BCE, a direct descendant of the Dukes of Sung who lived during the period 1766–1122 BCE. In Europe, due to the recording of numerous royal marriages, a surprising number of people can find their royal descent.

Where do you start? Genealogy has been described as a cross between a good detective story and a jigsaw puzzle. This book should serve as a guide through the adventure of compiling a family history. The importance of good record keeping is stressed. What you learn must be preserved for future generations. Once you begin your search you will perhaps meet relatives you never knew existed, or travel to places unknown to you. Many exciting experiences await you, so let us begin!

Genealogy and family history

As a family historian you must understand the difference between family history and genealogy. Genealogy studies pedigree, and establishes lines of descent. Genealogists' research goals are the names and dates proving and documenting genetic relationships. Although you will do some of this work, your goals as a family historian are rather different.

This book begins with you and your immediate family. You will record some genealogical information about each entry, but you will also give details of personal lives. This takes you beyond the concerns of the genealogist, who may only be incidentally interested in many fascinating family facts.

Genealogy gives the bare bones of people's descent and relationships; it is the interesting task of the family historian to put flesh on them. Once we know who Grandfather Clark's parents were, where and when he was born and died, who he married, and when and where each of his children was born, we have completed the genealogist's main work; indeed, these basic facts must be established

before we can do the family historian's work of giving some idea of what Grandfather Clark was really like.

Yet genealogical data gives many clues to an ancestor's life. Did he live through a war or some social upheaval? Did he die far from his birthplace? If so, why? The family historian uses genealogical clues to find answers. Think of your own life. It would be difficult for future generations to learn about you without some understanding of the times and places in which you have lived.

Compiling your family history is a deeply rewarding task. Future generations will learn about you and yours. They will enjoy your discoveries about more remote relatives. This book may prove more than a cherished heirloom: it could become the starting point for other people's research. So make your record as accurate and fully documented as possible.

Getting organized

What do you need before you start? First, a looseleaf notebook with paper. Make it your workbook. Write everything down in pencil in it before filling in this album.

Organizing your workbook helps avoid error. For example, the same first names often recur in families, sometimes within the same generation. Different people with the same names are easily confused. Avoid this by the simple system called "coding". If you turn to page 60 you will see the beginning of a sec-

tion called "Our Family Tree", which has spaces to record six generations of your and your spouse's families.

Now, in your workbook, designate one page to each person you are entering in the album. You can add more looseleaf sheets later as you need them. Each person should be identified by a three figure code telling at a glance their generation, and whether they are of your or your spouse's family, and giving them a personal number within their generation.

Sounds complicated, but it isn't really. Take yourself to begin with. You and your spouse are the first generation you are recording, so the first figure of your code is the number 1. And 1 will also be the first figure for your brothers and sisters and your brothers-in-law and sisters-in-law, and your first cousins.

The next generation you trace back to – that of your parents and uncles and aunts – will carry the first code number 2. Your four grandparents, and your spouse's, and all your spouse's and your great-aunts and great-uncles constitute the generation that starts its coding with the figure 3. Great-greats will start with a 4. That's easy enough, isn't it?

The next code entry is easier still. You don't need documents to know whether you are husband or wife in your marriage. And the second entry in the code is either an H or a W to sort out the two family lines leading down to your children. You and your partner, then, as the first-entered generation "Mr and Mrs" are

coded 1H and 1W. Husband's siblings and cousins are 1H and wife's are 1W. The husband's parents, aunts and uncles start coding 2H: the wife's are 2W. Grandparents and great-aunts and -uncles are 3W and 3H. And so on.

Finally every person entered has a personal number so that you know just which person in each generation is being described. Let's take you and your spouse first. You'll number yourselves 1, the first person on each side of the H and W division. So husband is fully coded 1H1; and wife is 1W1.

The husband's first sibling will become 1H2; the wife's 1W2. And so it goes through to your cousins. You might have first cousins who became 1W4 and 1W5; their parents, the wife's aunt and uncle might be 2W3 and 2W4, the wife's parents being 2W1 and 2W2.

You may find it helpful to lightly pencil these code numbers beside the spaces for names in the album. Then with a small number in the album and the same number heading a page in your workbook, you will know which data refer to which person and avoid confusion until your entry is complete and the pencil mark can be erased.

So make up your notebook pages with the code number at the top above the person's

name and personal data, and arrange the pages in code numerical order with dividers, if you like, separating the generations.

You will see that you don't have codes for your children and grandchildren. You don't need them. You know who they are and won't get them mixed up! Just make pages for each of them to put at the beginning or end of the notebook.

You will also need somewhere to file miscellaneous documents. These may be originals or copies of birth, marriage or death certificates. They may be letters or diaries, or various things you have acquired. "Family Sources" on page 94 gives a fuller list of what you might be storing.

Your miscellaneous file can be a large desk drawer, a filing cabinet or even a big box. Material filed in it should be organized with the same coding system as your notebook, and kept in numerical code order. Remember that even if information obtained about a family member cannot be used now, it may prove invaluable some day. Future generations may bless you for preserving something that may have seemed useless.

Photographs should have permanent identifying information recorded on their backs if it can be done without damaging the picture.

If this is impossible, have a copy made with a copier or by a photographic laboratory, and record the information there. It is well worth having all pictures copied anyway. At the least, you should record your information on a sheet of paper with the fullest possible description of the picture.

Your data should include the subject of the picture and its familial relationship to you. The relevant code number or numbers should be marked. When and where it was taken should be recorded if possible, and how you acquired it. You may wish to make extra copies to fix in this album, and any family photograph album, but do keep rare photographic originals safe; perhaps in a safety deposit box. They can be very precious indeed, and are usually irreplaceable.

Using Family Sources

Now, with your notebook and miscellaneous file prepared in the coded system, you are ready to start recording what you already know. Put it in the workbook first, and then copy it into this album. When you've filled in everything you know personally, you'll find you still need more data. On page 15 is a "Family History Questionnaire". Copy it and send it to all your family members, keeping a record of who has had it and when you sent it. A telephone call and an accompanying letter should help get their assistance. If you don't hear from anyone within a reasonable time, follow up with another call or letter. Don't forget to send them stamped addressed envelopes!

Some people may prefer a personal interview. Someone may have a Family Bible – an invaluable source for the family historian. Someone may know of a relative who has already compiled a family history. Usually at least one person has some mementos, and may not be aware of their value. Talk to as many people as you can to trace such additional family sources.

Soon you will regret not having asked some deceased relative questions only they could answer. When you approach the living, start with the eldest and be tactful and considerate. A personal visit is advisable: many old people are often not at their best on the telephone and can have difficulty in writing. Their memories may be hazy and too many questions can confuse them. It's best to write in advance explaining as simply as possible what you are doing and how they can help. Then telephone them asking when it would be convenient to visit.

Your visit will be more productive if you limit the number of questions you ask. Write down the information you want to obtain – names, dates, relationships – before you go. If your informant has no objection, it is well worth tape recording the interview, or having someone with you to take notes. If yourself keep stopping to write down what you hear, elderly people may lose their train of thought.

Sometimes relatives won't want to discuss certain family members or events – almost all families have their secrets!

Many old people tire easily, so it is often best to have several shorter sessions if possible. Take along any old photographs you may have for identification – they can jog the memory wonderfully! Remember also that you can interest your interviewees by telling them the things that you have already discovered. Do ask if they have any additional family source material as listed on page 94.

And always write a thank you letter afterwards!

The origin of your surname

The origin of surnames is a full-time occupation for some genealogists. You probably already know the derivation of your surname. But it is still worth referring to the *Oxford Dictionary of Surnames,* which can be found in most reference libraries. The further back you go in time, the rarer and more localized surnames will be. Very few families will find their names in the Domesday Book. Surnames were a fairly new idea in 1066, and were held only by the great landowners. The names usually signified the family home, though William the Conqueror's adversary, as we shall see, used a patronymic.

By the fifteenth century surnames were

fairly well established. They might be based on residence, such as York, Cornish, Hawksgill, or occupation (Butcher, Baker, Cooper), or physical appearance (Little, Rhead – abbreviating Redhead, or Pauncefoot – combining the old French words "*paunce fort*" meaning Big Belly). Nicknames and other such descriptive labels were also used.

Among the commonest in Northern Europe were patronymics identifying the holder as "son of" his father. The suffixes –son and –sen were common in Germanic languages. King Harold, loser of the battle of Hastings, took a patronymic surname from the famous earl who was his father, and was known as Harold Godwinson.

The Norman French variant was the prefix Fitz– (the same root as modern French *fils* or son). But after Charles II's prolific, promiscuous procreancy, this prefix was increasingly confined to illegitimate noblemen.

The Gaelic Mac, Mc and M' all signify "son of" as does the Welsh ap, often shortened to a single P as in Pritchard (ap Richard) or Price (ap Rhys).

Geographical distribution of your surname

Don't try this exercise if your name is Smith. There are about 800,000 of you listed in British telephone directories.

But if your name is not too common, pinpointing the areas of its geographical distribution can be a valuable clue to the family's place of origin. Remember that finding twenty entries in London is probably less significant than finding eight in a small village. It may be worthwhile contacting those eight. They may be distant relatives who can tell you a lot about your extended family.

Most public reference libraries in the United Kingdom have a complete set of telephone directories that you can use. Copy a map of the British Isles and record the number of listings in each directory. Then, on your map, colour in those areas with the largest name concentrations. The result may surprise you!

The old home visit

It can be an amazingly exciting experience to stand on the very spot where your ancestors once lived. Planning a visit carefully makes it even more rewarding. If possible, you will want to visit the old home site before all later generations of the family have moved away. Acquiring as much information as possible before you make your visit will contribute hugely to the value of your trip. Find out who lived there, how they made their living, where they worshipped and what part they played in the community. Contact the local reference library, the local history society, the local government offices, schools and places of worship before you go. They should provide you with much information and tell you what records are available for you to see. Make sure you plan your trip taking due note of the days when these resources are open for you to consult.

If family members still live in the area, be sure to inform them you are coming and plan to meet with them. Record your visit using as many means as possible. Take notes and photographs. A video-recording will be especially treasured by both present and future generations. If you are making a visit abroad, good planning is even more important. Contact the Embassy or High Commission of the country you intend to visit and enlist their help. You may need an interpreter and guide. But no matter where you go, thorough planning is essential.

Continuing your research

When you have gone as far as you can using family sources you will probably be intimidated by a mass of blank space at the end of your Family Tree. In fact, unless someone else in your family has undertaken extensive genealogical research, you will have found few if any of your great-great-grandparents, and no great-great-greats. They just aren't relatives any of us can remember!

There are three options you can now follow. You may decide to leave the album as it is for future generations to enjoy and add to if they wish. You might alternatively decide to employ a professional researcher to complete your work. Since this can be quite expensive it is vital that you hire a good and reliable agent. Most countries have a regulating body for researchers which should guarantee the quality of members' work. Consult one of the genealogical societies listed on page 95 for their guidance.

Before opting to continue the work yourself, it is best to read at least one introductory book on genealogical research. There are some suggestions on page 95. For those who have the dedication to carry it out, this can be a true labour of love. But whatever you choose to do, your completion of entries in this album has already accomplished something of great value to your family. Congratulations!

our Family

This album was researched and assembled by:

Name ....

When ....

Where ....

Family History

Name .... Date ....

1. What was your date of birth? ....

2. Where were you born? ....

3. What were your parents' full names at the time of your marriage? Your grandparents' names?

4. Who are your brothers and sisters, and when and where were they born?

5. What schools did you attend? Further education? Awards or honours?

6. What is your occupation? ....

7. What are your hobbies? ....

8. What is your religious affiliation? ....

9. If married, what was the full name of your spouse at the time of your marriage?

10. When and where did you marry? ....

11. Who attended your wedding? ....

12. Who was in your bridal party? ....

13. Where was your wedding reception? ....

14. How many children do you have? What are their names? When and where were they born?

15. Did you or any of your antecedents serve in the armed forces? If so, give details. ....

16. Do you know of any family members who have traced their forebears? ....

17. Please give all the information you have concerning our family history, including birth and death .. dates of family members.

18. Give the details of any family reunions or functions you may have attended.

19. Please include any additional information that you feel is relevant

Husband

Name ....

Place of birth ....

Mother's maiden name ....

Childhood home ....

Education ....

Occupation ....

Hobbies ....

Religious affiliation ....

Wife

Maiden name ....

Place of birth ....

Mother's maiden name ....

Childhood home ....

Education ....

Occupation ....

Hobbies ....

Religious affiliation ....

*Reader,
I married him.*

CHARLOTTE
BRONTE

17

our Wedding

Date ....

Place ....

Type of ceremony ....

Officiating minister or registrar ....

Best Man ....

Maid of Honour ....

Bridesmaids and pages ....

Organist or musicians ....

The Reception ....

Place ....

Lasted from .... to ....

Catered by ....

Speeches by ....

Music by ....

Memorable moments ....

....

....

*The bride hath
paced into the hall,
Red as a rose is she;
Nodding their heads
before her goes
The merry
minstrelsy.*

COLERIDGE

our Honeymoon

Where we went ....

From .... to ....

How we travelled ....

Where we stayed ....

What we did ....

....

....

Places we visited ....

....

What we enjoyed most ....

....

Come aboard for all the fun of France

Once aboard a great French Line ship to Europe, you are forever spoiled for any voyage less enchanting.

You find the very air sparkles with the fun-loving spirit of France. You relax to the French flair for elegant, gracious service. Your appetite revels in the French cuisine, recognized the world's f... with interesting new friends, to merr...

Almost with regret you a... ready for the sights and f...

REGULAR SAILINGS FROM NEW YORK:
The magnificent 51,840-ton **Liberté**, Sept. 1*, 18.
The gracious, storied **Ile de France**, Aug. 24, Sept. 11.
The intimate **Flandre**, Sept. 5, 24.
*On Sept. 1 the Liberté sails at 12:05 A.M.

21

our First home

*Home is home,
though it be never
so homely.*

JOHN CLARKE

We lived there from .... to ....

Address ....

Description ....

Improvements we made ....

Our neighbours were ....

*Lay thy sheaf
adown and come,
Share my harvest
and my home.*

THOMAS HOOD

later Moves

...our loves and comforts should increase Even as our days do grow!

SHAKESPEARE

Address ....

....

From .... to ....
Address ....

....

From .... to ....
Address ....

....

From .... to ....

our Professional life

Husband

EDUCATION

Schools attended and dates ....
....
....
....

Further education and dates ....
....

OCCUPATION

First job ....
Dates ....
Job description ....

Job ....
Dates ....
Job description ....

Job ....
Dates ....
Job description ....

$\mathcal{W}$IFE

EDUCATION

Schools attended with dates

....

....

....

....

Further education with dates ....

....

OCCUPATION

First job ....

Dates ....

Job description ....

Job ....

Dates ....

Job description ....

Job ....

Dates ....

Job description ....

*Women's
work is never done.*

<small>PROVERBIAL</small>

our Children

Name ....

Place of birth ....

Education ....

Hobbies ....

Occupation ....

Married to ....

Date of marriage ....

*God bless the
master of this house,
Likewise the
mistress too,
And all the
little children
That round the
table go:
Love and joy
come to you…*

WASSAILING SONG

26

Name ....

Place of birth ....

Education ....

Hobbies ....

Occupation ....

Married to ....

Date of marriage ....

Happy is the man that has his quiver full of children.

PSALM 127

❦

Name ....

Place of birth ....

Education ....

Hobbies ....

Occupation ....

Married to ....

Date of marriage ....

our Children

Name ....

Place of birth ....

Education ....

Hobbies ....

Occupation ....

Married to ....

Date of marriage ....

Thou art thy mother's glass, and she in thee Calls back the lovely April of her prime.

SHAKESPEARE

28

Name ....

Place of birth ....

Education ....

Hobbies ....

Occupation ....

Married to ....

Date of marriage ....

Name ....

Place of birth ....

Education ....

Hobbies ....

Occupation ....

Married to ....

Date of marriage ....

*Baby boy,
recognize your
mother with a smile.*
VIRGIL

Our Grandchildren

Name ....

Father ....

Mother ....

Birthdate ....

Name ....

Father ....

Mother ....

Birthdate ....

Name ....

Father ....

Mother ....

Birthdate ....

*Wisdom is
justified of her
children.*

MATTHEW, 11:19

Name ....

Father ....

Mother ....

Birthdate ....

Name ....

Father ....

Mother ....

Birthdate ....

our Grandchildren

…see the children
sport upon the shore,
And hear the
mighty waters rolling
evermore.

WORDSWORTH

Name ....

Father ....

Mother ....

Birthdate ....

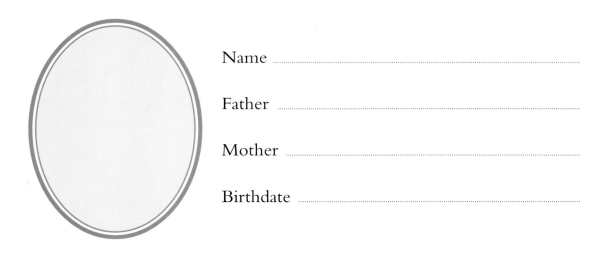

Name ....

Father ....

Mother ....

Birthdate ....

Name ....

Father ....

Mother ....

Birthdate ....

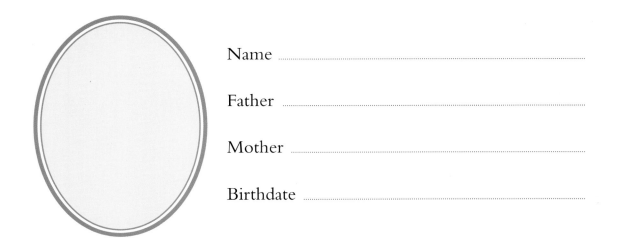

Name ....

Father ....

Mother ....

Birthdate ....

husband's Brothers

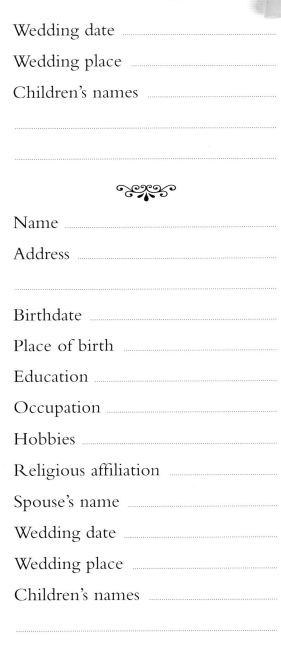

Name ....

Address ....

....

Birthdate ....

Place of birth ....

Education ....

Occupation ....

Hobbies ....

Religious affiliation ....

Spouse's name ....

Wedding date ....

Wedding place ....

Children's names ....

....

....

I've wandered east, I've wandered west Through many a weary way; But never, never can forget The love o' life's young day.

WILLIAM
MOTHERWELL

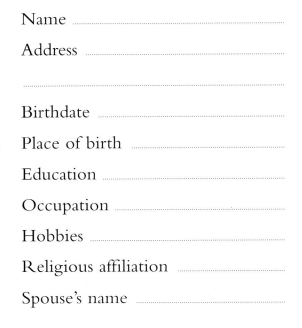

Name ....

Address ....

....

Birthdate ....

Place of birth ....

Education ....

Occupation ....

Hobbies ....

Religious affiliation ....

Spouse's name ....

Wedding date ....

Wedding place ....

Children's names ....

....

and *Sisters*

Name ....

Address ....

....

Birthdate ....

Place of birth ....

Education ....

Occupation ....

Hobbies ....

Religious affiliation ....

Spouse's name ....

Wedding date ....

Wedding place ....

Children's names ....

....

....

...there is no friend like a sister In calm or stormy weather.

CHRISTINA ROSSETTI

Place of birth ....

Education ....

Occupation ....

Hobbies ....

Religious affiliation ....

Spouse's name ....

Wedding date ....

Wedding place ....

Children's names ....

....

Name ....

Address ....

....

Birthdate ....

wife's Brothers

Name ....

Address ....

....

Birthdate ....

Place of birth ....

Education ....

Occupation ....

Hobbies ....

Religious affiliation ....

Spouse's name ....

Wedding date ....

Wedding place ....

Children's names ....

....

Name ....

Address ....

....

Birthdate ....

Place of birth ....

Education ....

....

Occupation ....

Hobbies ....

Religious affiliation ....

....

Spouse's name ....

Wedding date ....

Wedding place ....

Children's names ....

....

....

My sister and my sister's child, Myself and children three, Will fill the chaise; so you must ride On horseback after we.

WILLIAM COWPER

and *Sisters*

Name ....

Address ....

....

Birthdate ....

Place of birth ....

Education ....

Occupation ....

Hobbies ....

Religious affiliation ....

Spouse's name ....

Wedding date ....

Wedding place ....

Children's names ....

....

Name ....

Address ....

....

Birthdate ....

Place of birth ....

Education ....

Occupation ....

Hobbies ....

Religious affiliation ....

Spouse's name ....

Wedding date ....

Wedding place ....

Children's names ....

....

husband's Father

Name ....

Address ....

....

Birthdate ....

Birthplace ....

Education ....

Military service ....

Occupation ....

Hobbies ....

Religious affiliation ....

Wedding date and place ....

Mother's name ....

Father's name ....

*When all the
world is old, lad,
And all the trees
are brown....
God grant you find
one face there,
You loved when
all was young.*

CHARLES
KINGSLEY

*I grow old ever
learning many
things.*
SOLON

39

husband's Mother

Name _____

Address _____

_____

_____

Birthdate _____

Birthplace _____

Education _____

Occupation _____

Hobbies _____

Religious affiliation _____

Wedding date and place _____

Mother's name _____

Father's name _____

*In the dark room
where I began
My mother's life
made me a man
Through all the
months of
human birth
Her beauty fed my
common earth.*

JOHN MASEFIELD

wife's Father

Name

Address

Birthdate

Birthplace

Education

Military service

Occupation

Hobbies

Religious affiliation

Wedding date and place

Mother's name

Father's name

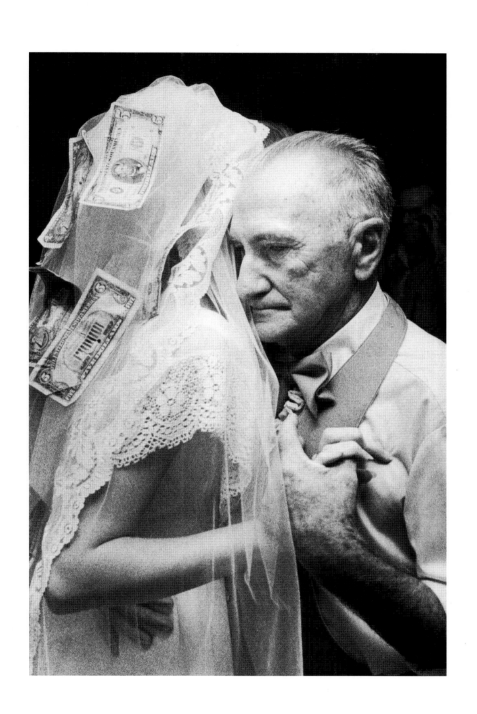

wife's Mother

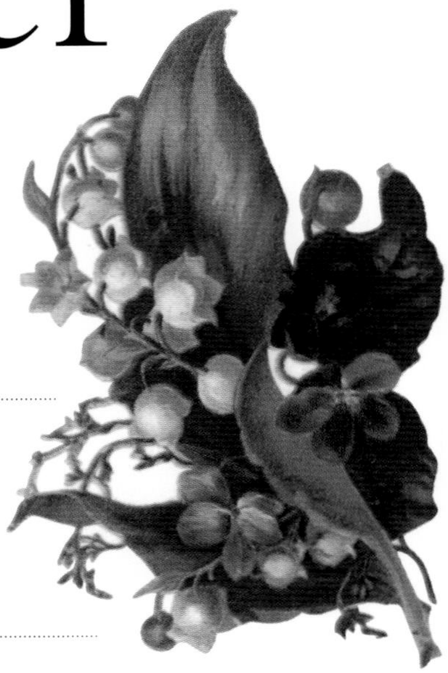

When you are old and gray and full of sleep,
And nodding by the fire, take down this book,
And slowly read, and dream of the soft look
Your eyes had once, and of their shadows deep.

W. B. Yeats

Name ....

Address ....

....

....

Birthdate ....

Birthplace ....

Education ....

Occupation ....

Hobbies ....

Religious affiliation ....

Wedding date and place ....

Mother's name ....

Father's name ....

They sin who tell us love can die. With life all other passions fly, All others are but vanity.

ROBERT SOUTHEY

husband's Aunts

Name ....

Address ....

....

Birthdate ....

Place of birth ....

Education ....

Occupation ....

Hobbies ....

Religious affiliation ....

Spouse's name ....

Wedding date ....

Wedding Place ....

Children's names ....

....

❧❧❧

Name ....

Address ....

....

Birthdate ....

Place of birth ....

Education ....

Occupation ....

Hobbies ....

Religious affiliation ....

Spouse's name ....

Wedding date ....

Wedding place ....

Children's names ....

....

❧❧❧

Name ....

Address ....

....

Birthdate ....

Place of birth ....

Education ....

Occupation ....

Hobbies ....

Religious affiliation ....

Spouse's name ....

Wedding date ....

Wedding place ....

Children's names ....

....

and *Uncles*

Name ....

Address ....

....

Birthdate ....

Place of birth ....

Education ....

Occupation ....

Hobbies ....

Religious affiliation ....

Spouse's name ....

Wedding date ....

Wedding place ....

Children's names ....

....

....

Name ....

Address ....

....

Birthdate ....

Place of birth ....

Education ....

Occupation ....

Hobbies ....

Religious affiliation ....

Spouse's name ....

Wedding date ....

Wedding place ....

Children's names ....

....

Name ....

Address ....

....

Birthdate ....

Place of birth ....

Education ....

Occupation ....

Hobbies ....

Religious affiliation ....

Spouse's name ....

Wedding date ....

Wedding place ....

Children's names ....

....

....

....

....

wife's Aunts

Name ....

Address ....

....

Birthdate ....

Place of birth ....

Education ....

Occupation ....

Hobbies ....

Religious affiliation ....

Spouse's name ....

Wedding date ....

Wedding place ....

Children's names ....

....

꧁ ꧂

Name ....

Address ....

....

Birthdate ....

Place of birth ....

Education ....

Occupation ....

Hobbies ....

Religious affiliation ....

Spouse's name ....

Wedding date ....

Wedding place ....

Children's names ....

꧁ ꧂

Name ....

Address ....

....

Birthdate ....

Place of birth ....

Education ....

Occupation ....

Hobbies ....

Religious affiliation ....

Spouse's name ....

Wedding date ....

Wedding place ....

Children's names ....

....

and $\mathcal{U}$ncles

Name ....

Address ....

....

Birthdate ....

Place of birth ....

Education ....

Occupation ....

Hobbies ....

Religious affiliation ....

Spouse's name ....

Wedding date ....

Wedding place ....

Children's names ....

....

....

❧

Name ....

Address ....

....

Birthdate ....

Place of birth ....

Education ....

Occupation ....

Hobbies ....

Religious affiliation ....

Spouse's name ....

Wedding date ....

Wedding place ....

Children's names ....

....

....

❧

Name ....

Address ....

....

Birthdate ....

Place of birth ....

Education ....

Occupation ....

Hobbies ....

Religious affiliation ....

Spouse's name ....

Wedding date ....

Wedding place ....

Children's names ....

....

Nice old geezer with a nasty cough, Sees my Missus, takes 'is topper off In a very gentlemanly way! Ma'am,' says he, ' I 'ave some news to tell, Your rich Uncle Tom of Camberwell Popped off recent, which it ain't a sell, Leaving you 'is little Donkey Shay.'

"Knocked 'em in the Old Kent Road"

MUSIC HALL SONG

❧

husband's Cousins

Name ....

Address ....

....

Birthdate ....

Place of birth ....

Education ....

Occupation ....

Hobbies ....

Religious affiliation ....

Spouse's name ....

Wedding date ....

Wedding place ....

Children's names ....

....

Name ....

Address ....

....

Birthdate ....

Place of birth ....

Education ....

Occupation ....

Hobbies ....

Religious affiliation ....

Spouse's name ....

Wedding date ....

Wedding place ....

Children's names ....

....

....

Name ....

Address ....

....

Birthdate ....

Place of birth ....

Father, Mother and Me, Sister and Auntie say All the people like us are We, And everyone else is They.

KIPLING

Name ....

Address ....

....

Birthdate ....

Place of birth ....

Education ....

Occupation ....

Hobbies ....

Religious affiliation ....

Spouse's name ....

Wedding date ....

Wedding place ....

Children's names ....

....

Name ....

Address ....

....

Birthdate ....

Place of birth ....

Education ....

Occupation ....

Hobbies ....

Religious affiliation ....

Spouse's name ....

Wedding date ....

Wedding place ....

Children's names ....

....

....

Name ....

Address ....

....

Birthdate ....

Place of birth ....

Education ....

Occupation ....

Hobbies ....

Religious affiliation ....

Spouse's name ....

Wedding date ....

Wedding place ....

Children's names ....

....

Name ....

Address ....

....

Birthdate ....

Place of birth ....

Education ....

Occupation ....

Hobbies ....

Religious affiliation ....

Spouse's name ....

Wedding date ....

Wedding place ....

Children's names ....

....

..close affection grows from common names, from kindred blood...

EDMUND BURKE

wife's Cousins

Name ....

Address ....

....

Birthdate ....

Place of birth ....

Education .... Wedding date ....

Occupation .... Wedding place ....

Hobbies .... Children's names ....

Religious affiliation ....

Spouse's name ....

Wedding date ....

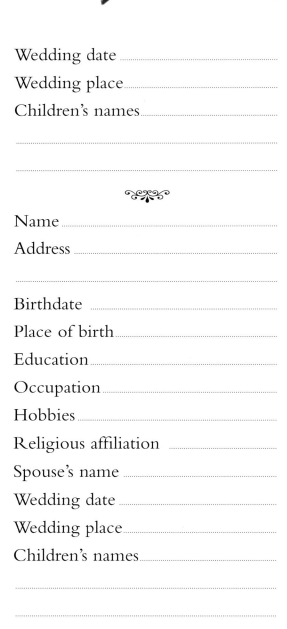

Wedding place ....

Children's names .... Name ....

Address ....

....

....

Name .... Birthdate ....

Address .... Place of birth ....

.... Education ....

Occupation ....

Birthdate .... Hobbies ....

Place of birth .... Religious affiliation ....

Education .... Spouse's name ....

Occupation .... Wedding date ....

Hobbies .... Wedding place ....

Religious affiliation .... Children's names ....

Spouse's name ....

....

O coz, coz, coz,
my pretty little coz,
that thou didst know
how many fathoms
deep I am in love!

SHAKESPEARE

Name

Address

Birthdate

Place of birth

Education

Occupation

Hobbies

Religious affiliation

Spouse's name

Wedding date

Wedding place

Children's names

❧❧❧

Name

Address

Birthdate

Place of birth

Education

Occupation

Hobbies

Religious affiliation

Spouse's name

Wedding date

Wedding place

Children's names

Name

Address

Birthdate

Place of birth

Education

Occupation

Hobbies

Religious affiliation

Spouse's name

Wedding date

Wedding place

Children's names

"Every day when he looked into the glass, and gave the last touch to his consummate toilette, he offered his grateful thanks to Providence that his family was not unworthy of him.

Disraeli

GRANDFATHER   GRANDMOTHER

One of the last dances was an old-fashioned country dance called 'the grandfather', when each couple in turn passed along holding a handkerchief, over which all the others had to jump.

PALL MALL MAGAZINE 1897

The markes which were in the body of the Grandfather do often appeare in the Grandchilde.

HELKIAH CROOKE

Name ....   Name ....

From .... to ....   From .... to ....

Birthplace ....   Birthplace ....

Occupation ....   Occupation ....

Wedding date and place

....

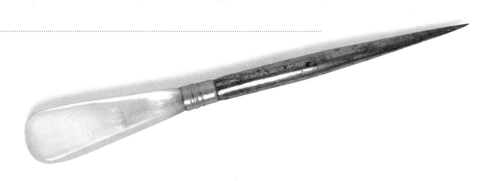

GRANDFATHER   GRANDMOTHER

Name..   Name..

From.................... to ....   From.................... to ....

Birthplace ....   Birthplace ....

Occupation ....   Occupation ....

Wedding date and place

....

You shall have nothing to do now but to be Grandmamma on satin cushions.
GEORGE ELIOT

What things were seen in granny's younger days?
JOHN CLARE

wifes's Grandparents

My
Grand-Daddy
is here tonight,
to the very
great satisfaction
of us all.

FANNY BURNEY

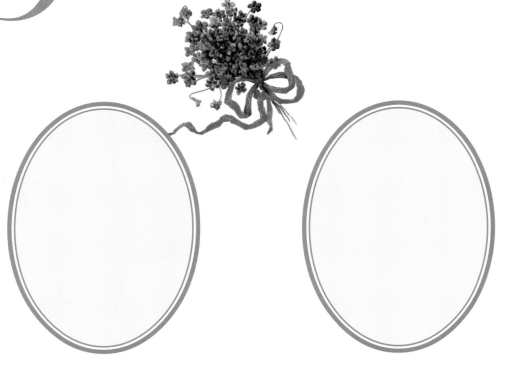

GRANDFATHER   GRANDMOTHER

Name ....   Name ....

From .... to ....   From .... to ....

Birthplace ....   Birthplace ....

Occupation ....   Occupation ....

Wedding date and place

....

GRANDFATHER

GRANDMOTHER

Name...

From .... to ....

Birthplace ....

Occupation ....

Name...

From .... to ....

Birthplace ....

Occupation ....

Wedding date and place

$\mathscr{I}$ our Immediate family

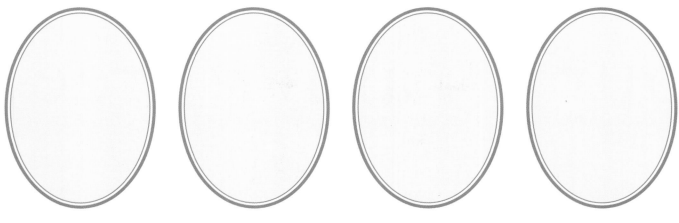

WIFE'S PARENTS   HUSBAND'S PARENTS

WIFE   HUSBAND

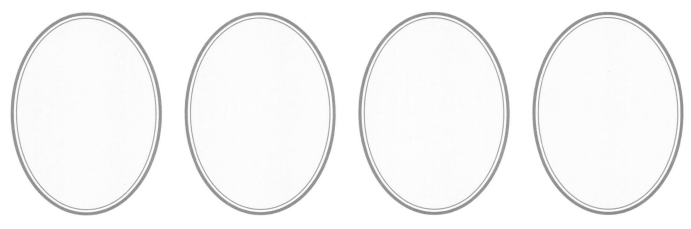

CHILDREN

our Family tree

Husband ....

Wife ....

Date of marriage ....

Place of marriage ....

Children ....

....

....

Husband's Father ....

Husband's Mother ....

Date of marriage ....

Place of marriage ....

Children ....

....

Wife's Father ....

Wife's Mother ....

Date of marriage ....

Place of marriage ....

Children ....

....

Husband's paternal Grandfather ....

Husband's paternal Grandmother ....

Date and place of marriage ....

Children ....

....

....

Husband's maternal Grandfather ....

Husband's maternal Grandmother ....

Date and place of marriage ....

Children ....

....

....

Wife's paternal Grandfather ....

Wife's paternal Grandmother ....

Date and place of marriage ....

Children ....

....

....

Wife's maternal Grandfather ....

Wife's maternal Grandmother ....

Date and place of marriage ....

Children ....

....

....

Husband's Great-Grandfather
....

Husband's Great-Grandmother
....

Husband's Great-Grandfather
....

Husband's Great-Grandmother
....

Husband's Great-Grandfather
....

Husband's Great-Grandmother
....

Husband's Great-Grandfather
....

Husband's Great-Grandmother
....

Husband's Great-Great-Grandfather
....

Husband's Great-Great-Grandmother
....

Husband's Great-Great-Grandfather
....

Husband's Great-Great-Grandmother
....

Husband's Great-Great-Grandfather
....

Husband's Great-Great-Grandmother
....

Husband's Great-Great-Grandfather
....

Husband's Great-Great Grandmother
....

Husband's Great-Great-Grandfather
....

Husband's Great-Great-Grandmother
....

Husband's Great-Great-Grandfather
....

Husband's Great-Great-Grandmother
....

Husband's Great-Great-Grandfather
....

Husband's Great-Great-Grandmother
....

Husband's Great-Great-Grandfather
....

Husband's Great-Great-Grandmother
....

Wife's Great-Great-Grandfather

Wife's Great-Great-Grandmother

Wife's Great-Grandfather

Wife's Great-Great-Grandfather

Wife's Great-Grandmother

Wife's Great-Great-Grandmother

Wife's Great-Great-Grandfather

Wife's Great-Grandfather

Wife's Great-Great-Grandmother

Wife's Great-Grandmother

Wife's Great-Great-Grandfather

Wife's Great-Great-Grandmother

Wife's Great-Great-Grandfather

Wife's Great-Grandfather

Wife's Great-Great-Grandmother

Wife's Great-Grandmother

Wife's Great-Great-Grandfather

Wife's Great-Great-Grandmother

Wife's Great-Grandfather

Wife's Great-Great-Grandfather

Wife's Great-Grandmother

Wife's Great-Great-Grandmother

Wife's Great-Great-Grandfather

Wife's Great-Great-Grandmother

Our great–great-great-

Mr and Mrs .... Née ....

Mr and Mrs .... Née ....

Mr and Mrs .... Née ....

Mr and Mrs .... Née ....

Mr and Mrs .... Née ....

Mr and Mrs .... Née ....

Mr and Mrs .... Née ....

Mr and Mrs .... Née ....

Mr and Mrs .... Née ....

Mr and Mrs .... Née ....

Mr and Mrs .... Née ....

Mr and Mrs .... Née ....

Mr and Mrs .... Née ....

Mr and Mrs .... Née ....

Mr and Mrs .... Née ....

Mr and Mrs .... Née ....

Mr and Mrs .... Née ....

Mr and Mrs .... Née ....

Mr and Mrs .... Née ....

Grandparents

Mr and Mrs .... Née ....

Mr and Mrs .... Née ....

Mr and Mrs .... Née ....

Mr and Mrs .... Née ....

Mr and Mrs .... Née ....

Mr and Mrs .... Née ....

Mr and Mrs .... Née ....

Mr and Mrs .... Née ....

Mr and Mrs .... Née ....

Mr and Mrs .... Née ....

Mr and Mrs .... Née ....

Mr and Mrs .... Née ....

Mr and Mrs .... Née ....

Our great–
great-great–

Mr and Mrs .... Née ....

Mr and Mrs .... Née ....

Mr and Mrs .... Née ....

Mr and Mrs .... Née ....

Mr and Mrs .... Née ....

Mr and Mrs .... Née ....

Mr and Mrs .... Née ....

Mr and Mrs .... Née ....

Mr and Mrs .... Née ....

Mr and Mrs .... Née ....

Mr and Mrs .... Née ....

Mr and Mrs .... Née ....

Mr and Mrs .... Née ....

Mr and Mrs .... Née ....

Mr and Mrs .... Née ....

Mr and Mrs .... Née ....

Mr and Mrs .... Née ....

Mr and Mrs .... Née ....

Mr and Mrs .... Née ....

Grandparents

Mr and Mrs .... Née ....

Mr and Mrs .... Née ....

Mr and Mrs .... Née ....

Mr and Mrs .... Née ....

Mr and Mrs .... Née ....

Mr and Mrs .... Née ....

Mr and Mrs .... Née ....

Mr and Mrs .... Née ....

Mr and Mrs .... Née ....

Mr and Mrs .... Née ....

Mr and Mrs .... Née ....

Mr and Mrs .... Née ....

Mr and Mrs .... Née ....

our Ancestors

Name ....

Place of origin ....

Additional information ....

....

....

Name ....

Place of origin ....

Additional information ....

....

....

Name ....

Place of origin ....

Additional information ....

....

....

Name ....

Place of origin ....

Additional information ....

....

....

Afoot and light-hearted I take to the open road, Healthy, free, the world before me.

WALT WHITMAN

Name ....

Place of origin ....

Additional information ....

....

....

Name ....

Place of origin ....

Additional information ....

....

....

...tired with the labour of far travel we have come to our own home and rest on the couch we have longed for.

Catullus

Name ....

Place of origin ....

Additional information ....

....

....

Name ....

Place of origin ....

Additional information ....

....

....

our Family name

What does our surname mean?

....

....

....

....

....

From what language does it originate?

....

....

....

....

Has it been Anglicized from an original version, or changed in any other way from an older form?

....

....

....

....

....

Is it spelled in any other ways?

....

....

....

....

Are there any famous people bearing our surname?

....

....

....

....

our First names

Bright with names that men remember, loud with names that men forget.

SWINBURNE

Name ....

What does this name mean? ....

Additional information ....

....

....

....

Name ....

What does this name mean? ....

Additional information ....

....

....

....

Name ....

What does this name mean? ....

Additional information ....

....

....

....

Name ....

What does this name mean? ....

Additional information ....

....

....

....

Name ....

What does this name mean? ....

Additional information ....

....

....

....

Name ....

What does this name mean? ....

Additional information ....

....

....

....

family Weddings

Bride ....

Groom ....

Place and date ....

Bride's parents ....

Attendants ....

Place of reception ....

Guests ....

....

....

Bride ....

Groom ....

Place and date ....

Bride's parents ....

Attendants ....

Place of reception ....

Guests ....

....

....

Bride ....

Groom ....

Place and date ....

Bride's parents ....

Attendants ....

Place of reception ....

Guests ....

....

....

Hail wedded love,
mysterious law,
true source
Of human offspring,
sole propriety,
In Paradise of all
things common else.

Milton

Bride ....
Groom ....
Place and date ....
Bride's parents ....
Attendants ....
Place of reception ....
Guests ....
....
....

Bride ....
Groom ....
Place and date ....
Bride's parents ....
Attendants ....
Place of reception ....
Guests ....
....
....

Says John, It is
my wedding day,
And all the world
would stare,
If wife should dine
at Edmonton,
And I should dine
at Ware.
WILLIAM COWPER

family Reunions

When was it held ....
Where ....
Were there special activities? ....

....

Who attended? ....

....

....

....

....

When was it held ....
Where ....
Were there special activities? ....

....

Who attended? ....

....

....

....

....

When was it held ....
Where ....
Were there special activities? ....

....

Who attended? ....

....

....

....

....

When was it held ....
Where ....
Were there special activities? ....
....
Who attended? ....
....
....
....
....

When was it held ....
Where ....
Were there special activities? ....
....
Who attended? ....
....
....
....
....

*Is it a party
in a parlour?
Cramm'd just as
they on earth
were cramm'd -
Some sipping punch,
some sipping tea,*

WORDSWORTH

family Reunions

When was it held ....
Where ....
Were there special activities? ....
....
Who attended? ....
....
....
....
....

When was it held ....
Where ....
Were there special activities? ....
....
Who attended? ....
....
....
....
....

When was it held ....
Where ....
Were there special activities? ....
....
Who attended? ....
....
....
....

When was it held ....

Where ....

Were there special activities? ....

....

Who attended? ....

....

....

....

....

When was it held ....

Where ....

Were there special activities? ....

....

Who attended? ....

....

....

....

family Holidays

Date ....

Place ....

....

....

Date ....

Place ....

....

....

Date ....

Place ....

....

....

family Holidays

Where we went ....

When .... to ....

How we travelled ....

Where we stayed ....

What we did ....

....

....

Where we went ....

When .... to ....

How we travelled ....

Where we stayed ....

What we did ....

....

....

Where we went ....

When .... to ....

How we travelled ....

Where we stayed ....

What we did ....

....

....

Where we went ....

When .... to ....

How we travelled...

Where we stayed ....

What we did ....

....

....

important Times

What historical events in your lifetime have affected you most?

in our lives

*Fond Memory
brings the light
Of other days
around me;*

THOMAS MOORE

Have either of you ever met any famous people?

important Times

What has been the most exciting time you can remember?

What have been your happiest times, and why?

the Old home visit

What town or city did you visit? ....

Who lived there? ....

When .... to ....

Address ....

What town or city did you visit? ....

Who lived there? ....

When .... to ....

Address ....

What town or city did you visit? ....

Who lived there? ....

When .... to ....

Address ....

What town or city did you visit? ....

Who lived there? ....

When .... to ....

Address ....

*Such is
the patriot's boast,
where'er we roam,
His first,
best country ever
is at home.*

OLIVER GOLDSMITH

Do any family members still live in these places?

....

....

....

....

If the family has all moved away, why? ....

....

Are any of your old family homes still standing? ....

....

....

....

....

What were these places like when your family lived there? Have they changed much? What part did the family play in the life of these communities? How did they earn their living?

....

....

....

....

....

....

....

the Old home visit

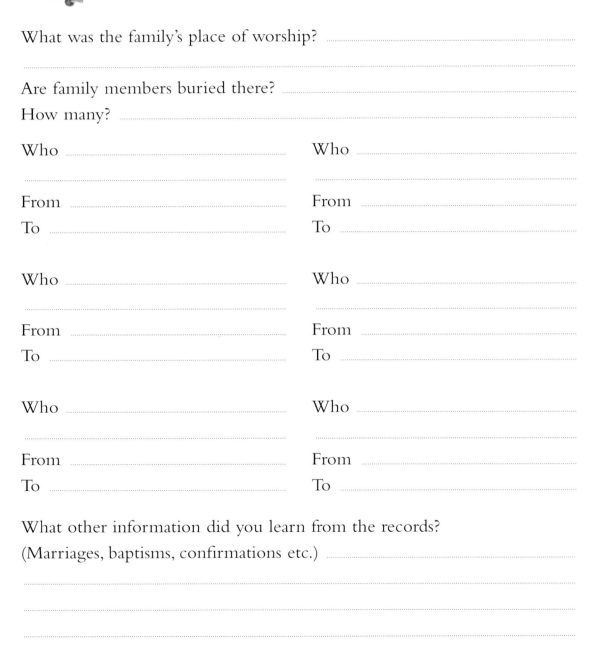

What was the family's place of worship? ....
....

Are family members buried there? ....
How many? ....

Who	Who ....
From	From ....
To	To ....
Who	Who ....
From	From ....
To	To ....
Who	Who ....
From	From ....
To	To ....

What other information did you learn from the records?
(Marriages, baptisms, confirmations etc.) ....
....
....
....

a Record of your visits

Photographs

Homes ....

....

Land ....

Home site. ....

Area ....

Places of worship ....

Cemetery ....

Family business ....

Family members still there ....

....

Video contents ....

....

....

Tape recordings contents ....

....

Copies ....

Maps ....

Religious records ....

Civic records ....

Additional information:

....

....

....

Special memories

Name ....

Family relationship ....

From .... to ....

Place of burial ....

Name ....

Family relationship ....

From .... to ....

Place of burial ....

Name ....

Family relationship ....

From .... to ....

Place of burial ....

Name ....

Family relationship ....

From .... to ....

Place of burial ....

*Beneath those
rugged elms,
that yew-tree's shade,
Where heaves the
turf in many a
mouldering heap,
Each in his narrow
cell forever laid,
The rude forefathers
of the hamlet sleep.*

THOMAS GRAY

92

Name ....

Family relationship ....

From .... to ....

Place of burial ....

Name ....

Family relationship ....

From .... to ....

Place of burial ....

Name ....

Family relationship ....

From .... to ....

Place of burial ....

Name ....

Family relationship ....

From .... to ....

Place of burial ....

The glories of our blood and state Are shadows, not substantial things; There is no armour against fate; Death lays his icy hand on kings: Sceptre and crown Must tumble down, And in the dust be equal made With the poor crooked scythe and spade.

JAMES SHIRLEY

useful Names
and addresses

ADDITIONAL FAMILY SOURCES

Address books and lists
Albums, Photographs etc.
Autograph books
Awards
Baby books
Baptismal or Christening records
    Bar Mitzvah or Bas Mitzvah
    records
Bible entries
Biographical notes
Birth announcements
Birth certificates
Birthday books
Books (clippings, inscriptions, etc.)
Business records
Certificates
Church membership records
Citizenship papers
Club and Society records
Confirmation records
Congratulatory messages
Death certificates and burial
    records
Deeds
Diaries
Diplomas
Education and school records:
    reports, awards, certificates,
    registers

Employment records
Engagement announcements
Family associations
Family trees and charts
Funeral memorial cards
Genealogies (unpublished)
House/land purchases or sales
Insurance records, leases and
    rents
Legal papers and solicitors'
    letters
Ledgers
Letters
Licenses
Life sketches (unpublished)
Maps
Marriage certificates, contracts,
    licences and settlements
Membership certificates: Boy
    Scouts, lodges, political
    parties, etc
Mementoes
Memorials
Military records: citations,
    conscription burial or
    cemetery records, discharge,
    orders, pensions, veterans'
    benefits, etc.
Mortgages

Naturalization papers
Newspapers and clippings
Notebooks
Obituaries
Oral family history and traditions
Passports and applications
Photographs and names on front
    and back of the same
Pictures
Portraits and paintings
Professional certificates (teaching,
    pharmacy, etc.)
Promotion notices
Receipts
Retirement/Superannuation
    records
Souvenirs
Surveys of property
Tax Bills, receipts and returns
Telegrams
Telephone number lists
Tombstone inscriptions
University and college records:
    Degree and graduation
    certificates and lists
Wills and probate documents
Yearbooks (school, university,
    church etc.)

USEFUL ADDRESSES

General Register Office
St Catherine's House
10 Kingsway
London WC2B 6JP

General Register Office, Scotland
New Register House
Edinburgh EH1 3YT

General Register Office, Northern Ireland
49-55 Chichester Street
Belfast BT1 4HL

Public Record Office
Ruskin Avenue
Kew
Richmond
Surrey TW9 4DW

Scottish Record Office
New Register House
Edinburgh EH1 3YT

Public Records Office
66 Balmoral Avenue
Belfast BT9 6NY

Genealogical Library of the Latter Day Saints
64-68 Exhibition Road
London SW7

Institute of Heraldic and Genealogical Studies
Northgate
Canterbury
Kent CT1 1BA

Federation of Family History Societies
96 Beaumont Street
Milehouse
Plymouth PL2 3AD

Society of Genealogists
14 Charterhouse Buildings
London EC1

RECOMMENDED BOOKS

★ C.R.Humphery-Smith,
   Introducing Family History,
   Institute for Heraldic and Genealogical
   Studies, 1996.

Stella Colwell,
The Family History Book
(2nd edition) Phaidon, 1989.

A.J.Willis and M.Tatchell,
Genealogy for Beginners,
Phillimore, 1984.

Noel Currer-Briggs and
Royston Gambier
Debrett's Family Historian,
Webb and Bower, 1981.

David Hey,
The Oxford Guide to Family History,
Oxford University Press, 1993.

D.M.Field,
Tracing Your Ancestors,
Treasure Press, 1987.

★ Highly recommended

Credits

SELECT BIBLIOGRAPHY

Sir William Addison, *Understanding English Surnames*, Batsford, 1978

Stella Colwell, *The Family History Book*, (2nd edn), Phaidon, 1989

Noel Currer-Briggs & Royston Gambier, *Debrett's Family Historian*, Webb & Bower, 1981

Patrick Hanks & Frances Hodges, *The Dictionary of Surnames*, Oxford University Press, 1989

N.T.Hansen, *Guide to Genealogical Sources – Australia and New Zealand*, 1963

David Hey, *The Oxford Guide to Family History*, Oxford University Press, 1993

C.R.Humphery-Smith, *Introducing Family History*, Institute for Heraldic and Genealogical Studies, 1996

M.Rubincam, *Genealogical Research Methods and Sources*, Genealogical Publications, 1966

Meg Wheeler, *Tracing your Roots*, Tiger International plc, 1996

ACKNOWLEDGEMENTS

The authors would like to thank Jeremy Palmer, B.A. and Richard Baxter Ph D., D.I.C., F.H.G. of the Institute of Heraldic and Genealogical Studies and the staff of the Guildhall Library, London.

In addition our agent, Richard Jeffs of Roger Hancock Ltd, and our editor, Sarah Larter of Carlton Books have been their usual fund of help and encouragement, and Paul Savory, as ever, has helped in more ways than we can count.

The publishers would like to thank the following sources for their kind permission to reproduce the pictures in this book:

CORBIS: /Tony Arruza 22b /Bettmann 23, 32, 45, 84 /©Werner Forman 68, 69 /Philip Gould 43, 55t/Hulton Deutsch Collection 18, 28, 37, 77 /Library of Congress 57t, 85 /Richard T. Nowitz 91/Oscar White 75; DOVER PUBLICATIONS: 2t, 4, 5tr, 6, 9tr, 10, 13, 19t, 20t, 29cr, 35bl, 40, 44, 52, 54, 56, 59, 64, 66tl, 74, 76, 88, 89, 90, 95; MARY EVANS PICTURE LIBRARY: 3, 21t, 25, 26, 34b, 35, 41, 58, 80, 83, 86; HULTON-GETTY: 39; ROBERT OPIE COLLECTION: 36.